# DR. PAULAHA

# THE TRIANGLE AND
# THE BEAUTIFUL CIRCLE

Edited by Katharine Elizabeth Paulaha

Copyright © 2006 by Dennis F. Paulaha.
All rights reserved. No part of this book may be reproduced or transmitted in any form or by any means—electronic or mechanical, including photocopying, recording, or any information storage and retrieval system—without permission in writing from the publisher.

Printed in the United States of America
I H G F E D C B A

First published by Dennis F. Paulaha

ISBN 0-9723619-2-8

PATRON BOOKS

For Katharine and Sarah

## A Note From the Author

We cannot change the past.
We cannot get back what is gone.
We can only go forward, inch by inch, step by step, from where we are today.
So choose well, dear reader.

Once,
there
was
a
little
triangle.

The
little
triangle
was
very
happy.

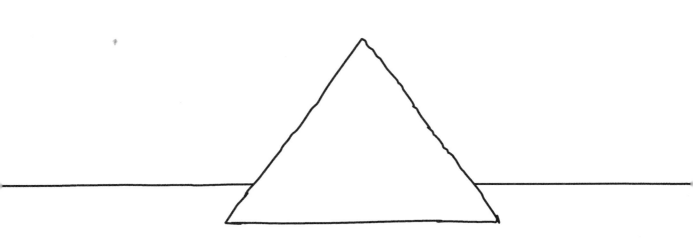

A
tall
triangle
bought
the
little
triangle
everything
the
little
triangle
wanted,

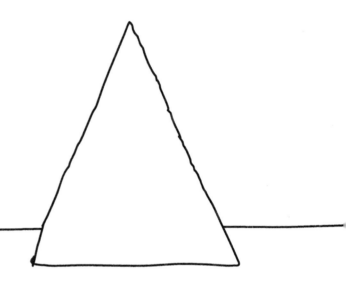

because
everything
the
little
triangle
wanted
seemed
very
inexpensive
to
the
tall
triangle.

The
little
triangle
asked
for
some
squares.

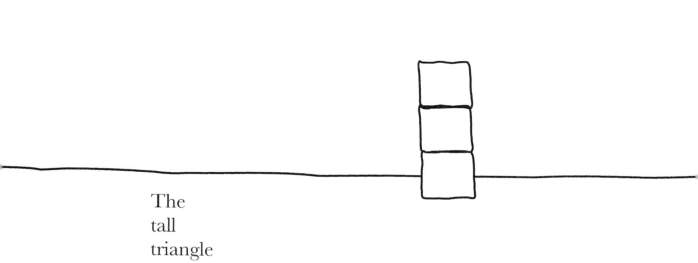

The
tall
triangle
bought
the
little
triangle
some
squares.

The
little
triangle
asked
for
a
rectangle.

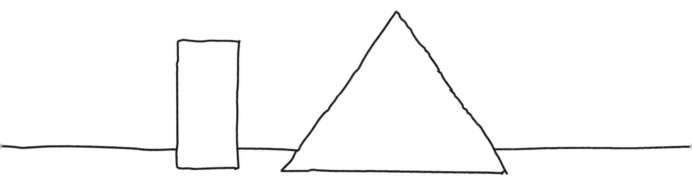

The
tall
triangle
bought
the
little
triangle
a
rectangle.

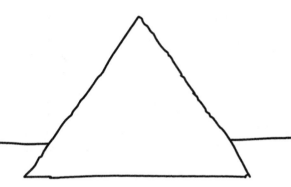

The
little
triangle
had
many
toys
and
many
other
little
triangles
to
play
with.

Some
of
the
other
little
triangles
had
toys
that
were
different
from
his.

Sometimes
the
little
triangle
thought
it
would
be
fun
to
have
some
of
the
other
toys.

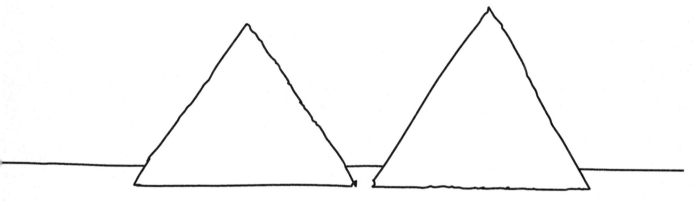

But
the
little
triangle
was
happy
with
what
he
had.

One
day,
the
little
triangle
saw
a
beautiful
circle.

"Oh, if only I could have that beautiful circle,"
the
little
triangle
thought.

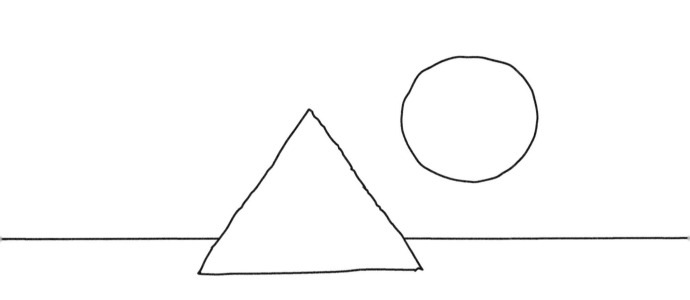

The
little
triangle
told
the
tall
triangle
how
happy
he
would
be
if
he
had
the
beautiful
circle.

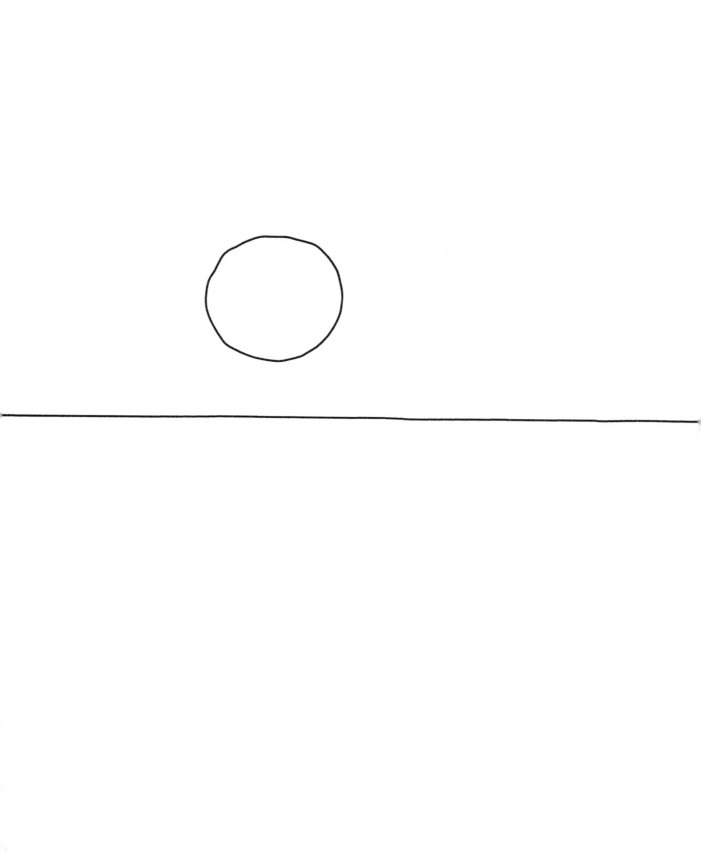

"Can't do it,"
the
tall
triangle
said.
"The circle is too expensive."

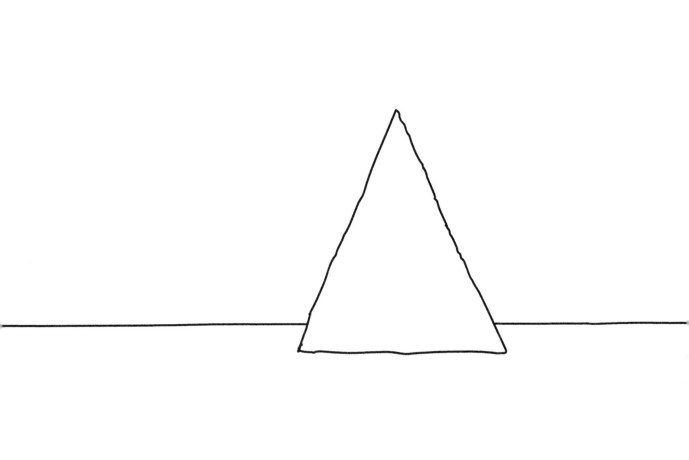

"Oh, please,"
the
little
triangle
cried.

The
little
triangle
asked
again
and
again
for
the
beautiful
circle.

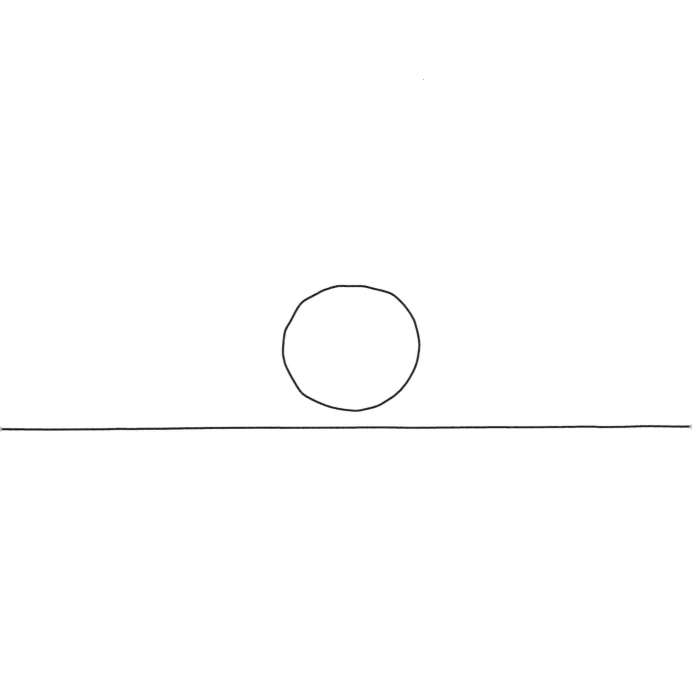

And
the
tall
triangle
always
said,
"No."

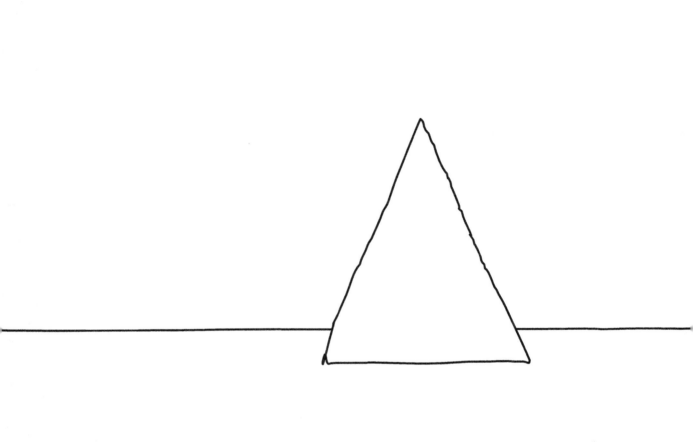

The
little
triangle
was
sad.

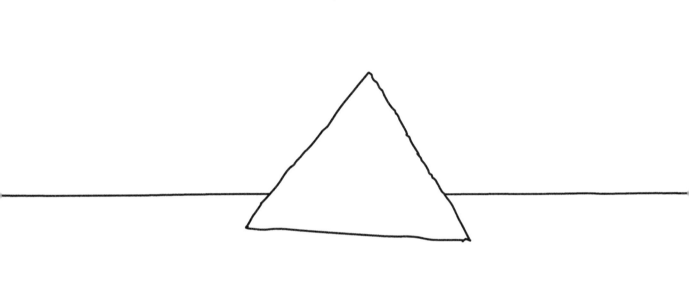

Finally,
the
tall
triangle
said,
"I cannot buy the beautiful circle for you,
but I will give you a weekly allowance.
Then you will have your own money, and
you can buy whatever you choose."

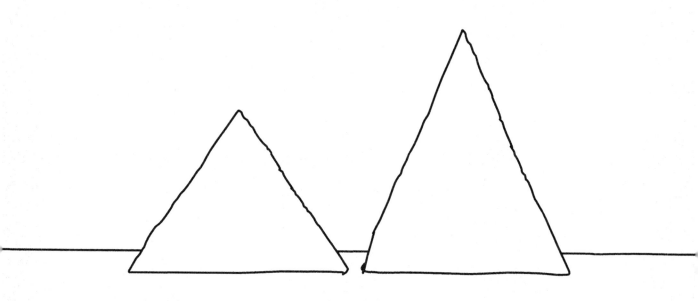

The
little
triangle
was
happy
again.

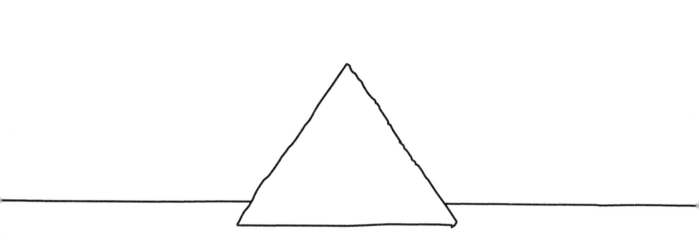

The
little
triangle
took
the
allowance
to
the
store
to
buy
the
beautiful
circle.

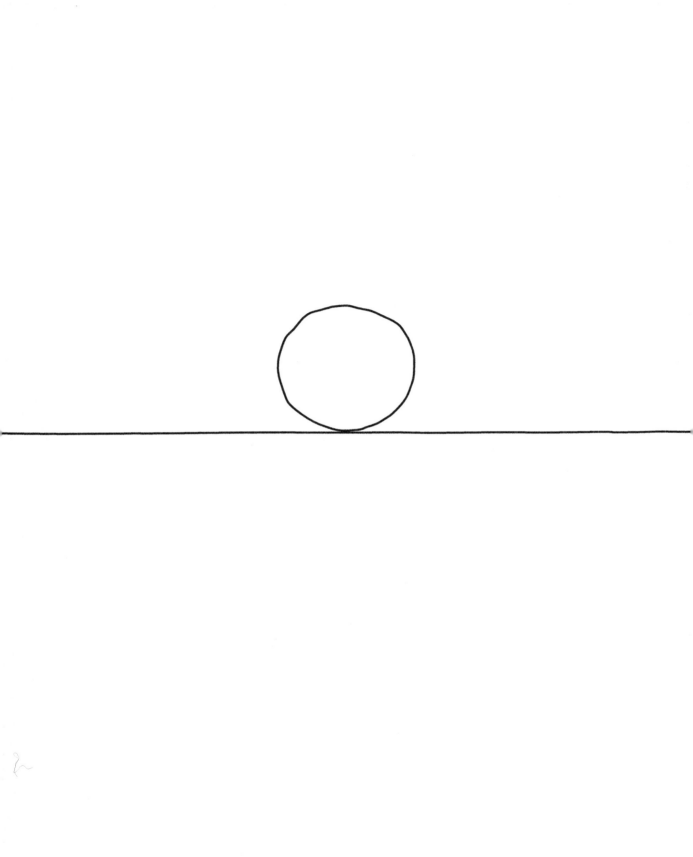

But
it
was
not
enough.

While
the
little
triangle
was
at
the
store,
the
little
triangle
saw
an
oval.

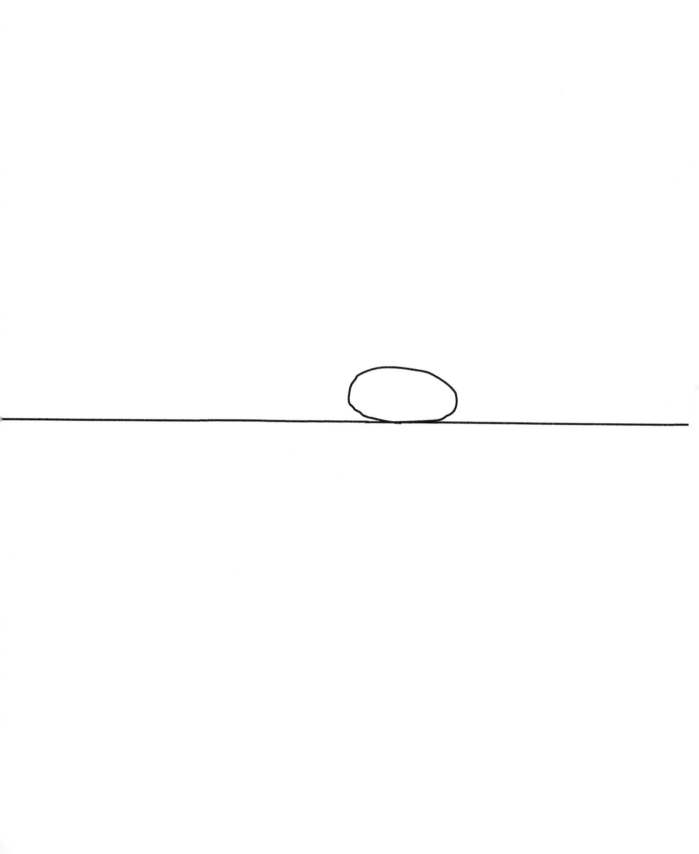

"That oval is not nearly as nice as the beautiful
circle,"
the
little
triangle
thought.
"But I can buy the oval because it doesn't cost
very much."

And
that
is
what
he
did.

The
little
triangle
bought
the
oval.

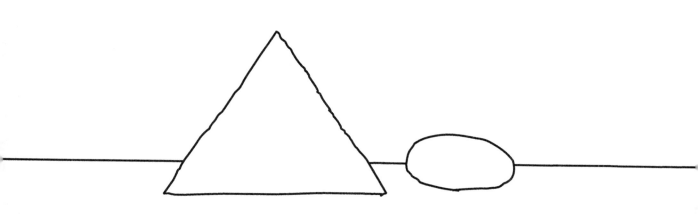

And
the
oval
made
the
little
triangle
happy…
for
a
while.

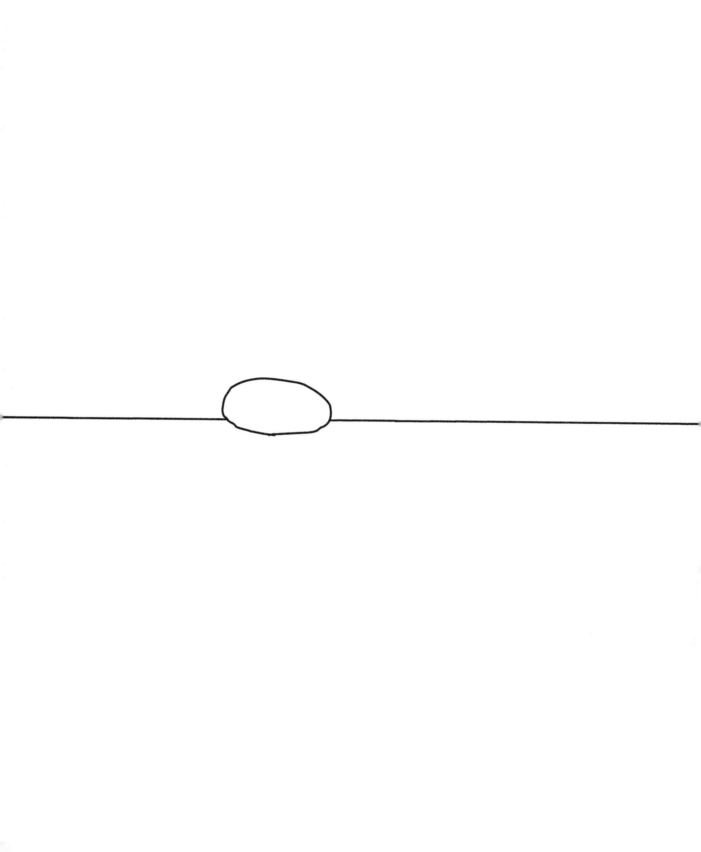

Each
Saturday,
the
little
triangle
took
his
allowance
to
the
store.

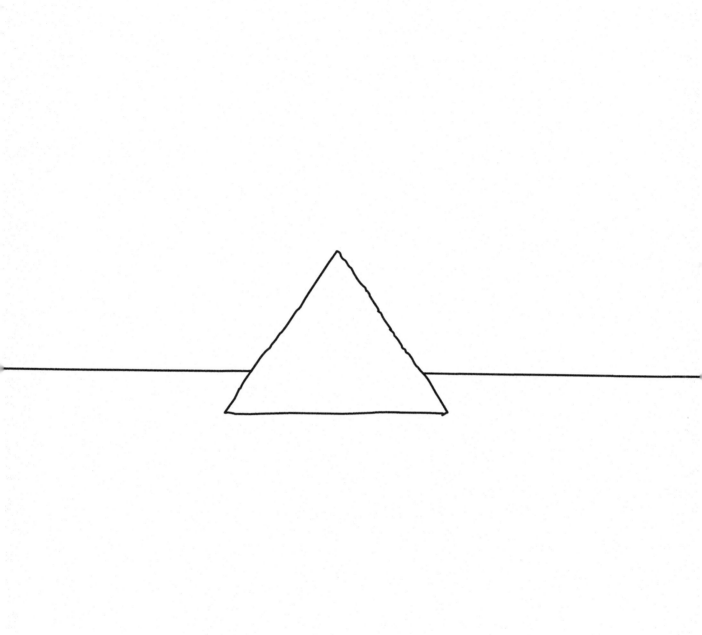

Each
Saturday,
the
owner
of
the
store
told
the
little
triangle
he
did
not
have
enough
money
to
buy
the
beautiful
circle.

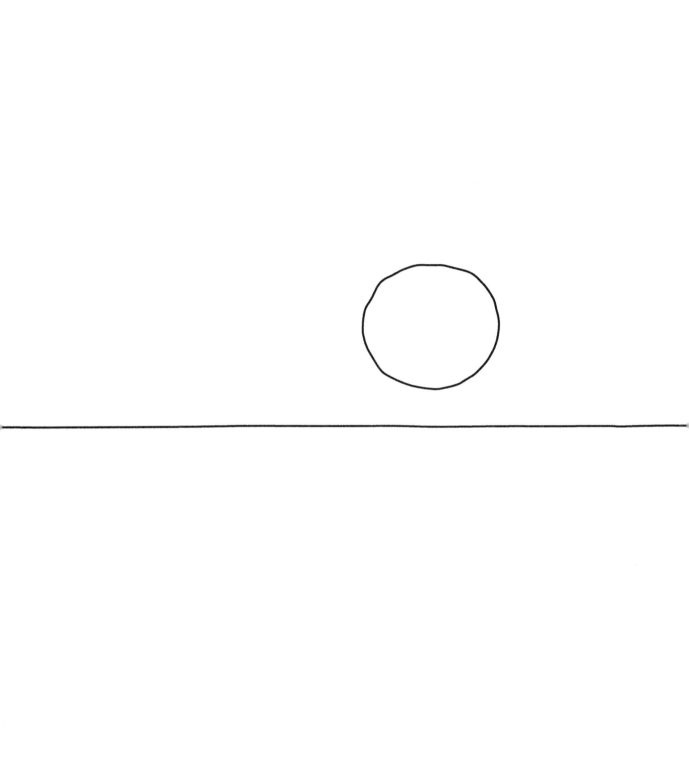

Each
Saturday,
the
little
triangle
bought
something
he
could
afford.

The
little
triangle
bought
pentagons,

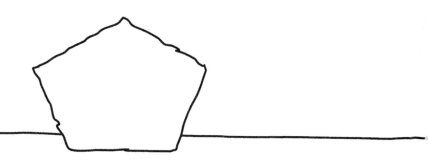

hexagons,

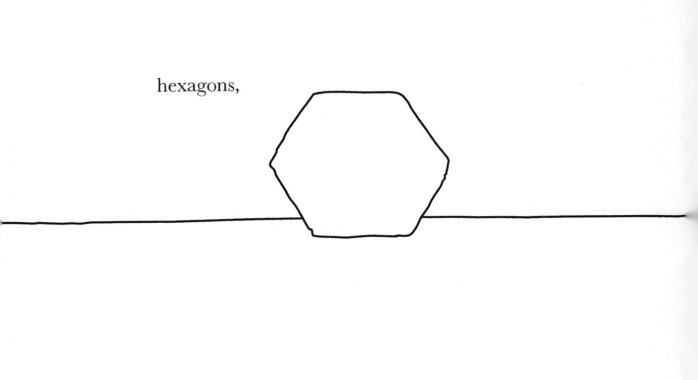

octagons,

and diamonds.

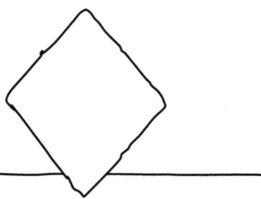

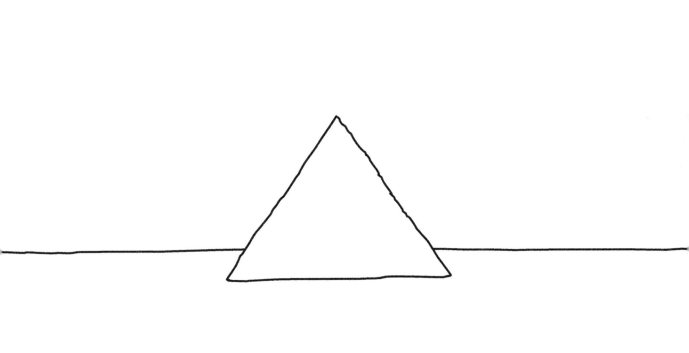

The
little
triangle
grew
older
and
taller.

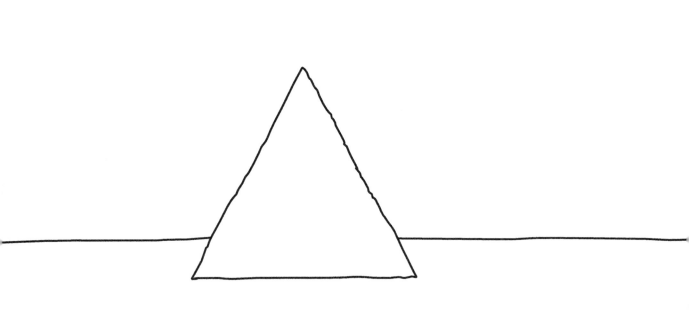

Again
and
again,
the
little
triangle
asked
the
tall
triangle
to
please
buy
the
beautiful
circle.

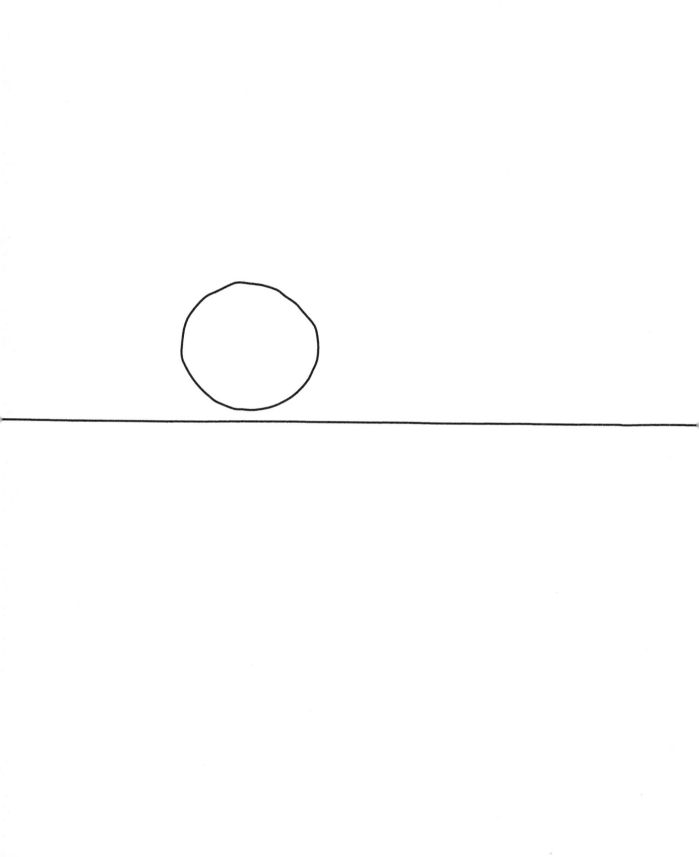

But
the
tall
triangle
always
said,
"No."

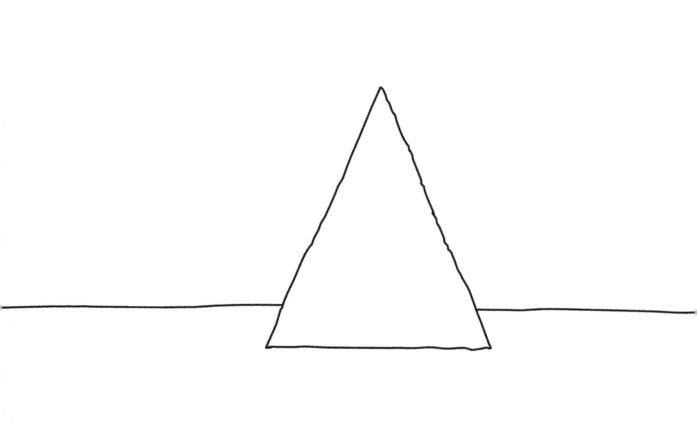

One
day,
the
tall
triangle
said,
"I can't buy the beautiful circle for you. But now
that you are older, I will give you a larger
allowance."

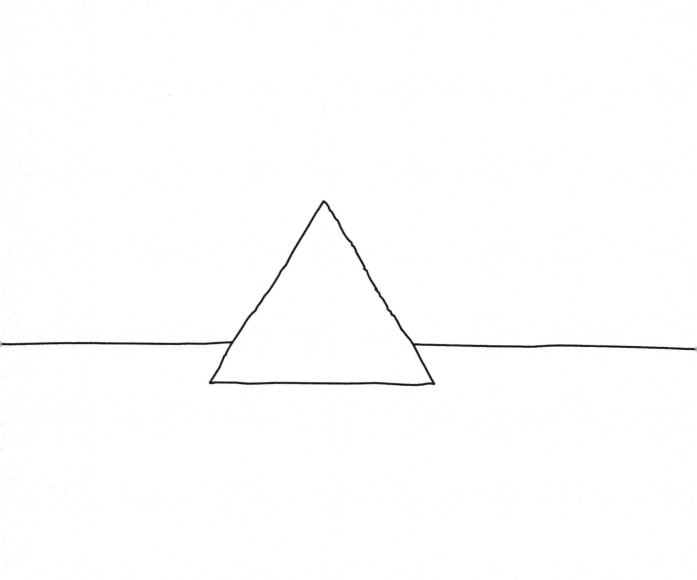

But
the
larger
allowance
was
still
not
enough
to
buy
the
beautiful
circle.

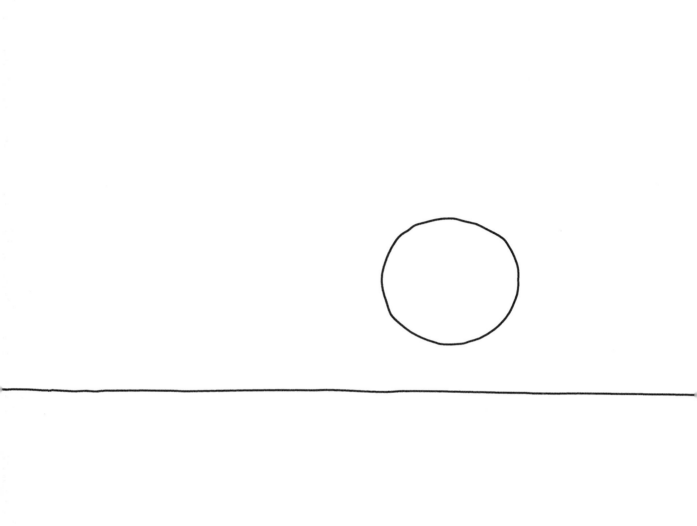

So
the
little
triangle
bought
more
squares,
rectangles,
ovals,
pentagons,
hexagons,
and octagons.

And
the
squares,
rectangles,
ovals,
pentagons,
hexagons,
and octagons,
always
made
him
happy…
for
a
while.

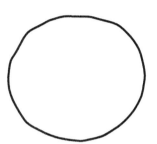

Then
the
little
triangle
would
once
again
think
about
the
beautiful
circle.

When
the
little
triangle
was
old
enough,
he
got
a
job
and
bought
many
things.

But
he
was
not
happy.

He
did
not
have
anything
he
liked
as
much
as
the
beautiful
circle.

And
the
little
triangle
never
had
enough
money
at
one
time
to
buy
the
beautiful
circle.

The
years
passed,
and
the
little
triangle
grew
old.

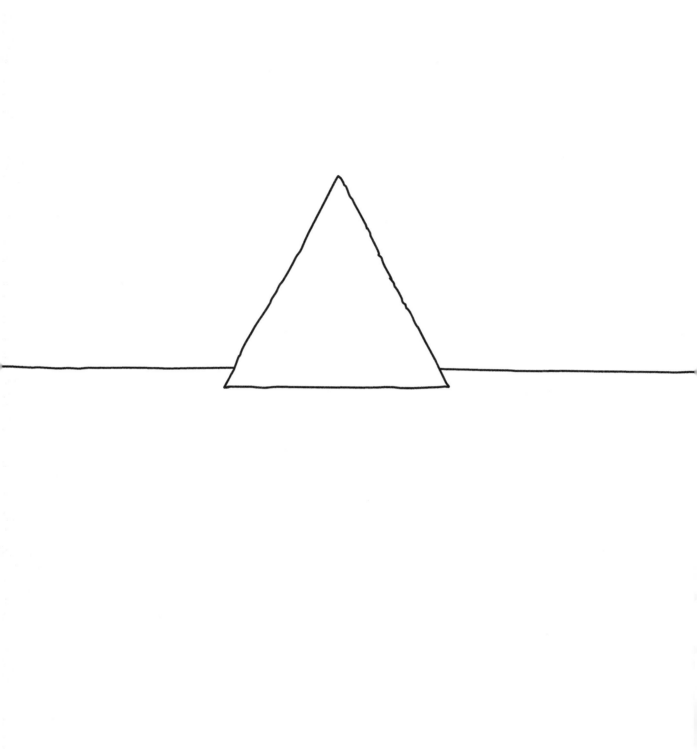

But
he
never
stopped
dreaming
of
the
beautiful
circle.

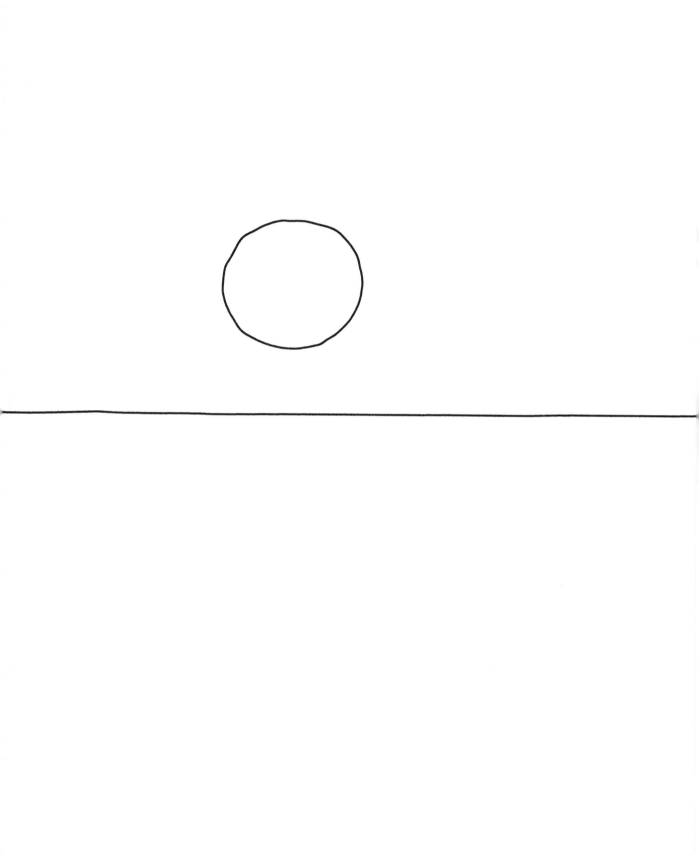

One
day
the
little
old
triangle
said,
"I wish I could trade all the things I bought
for the beautiful circle."

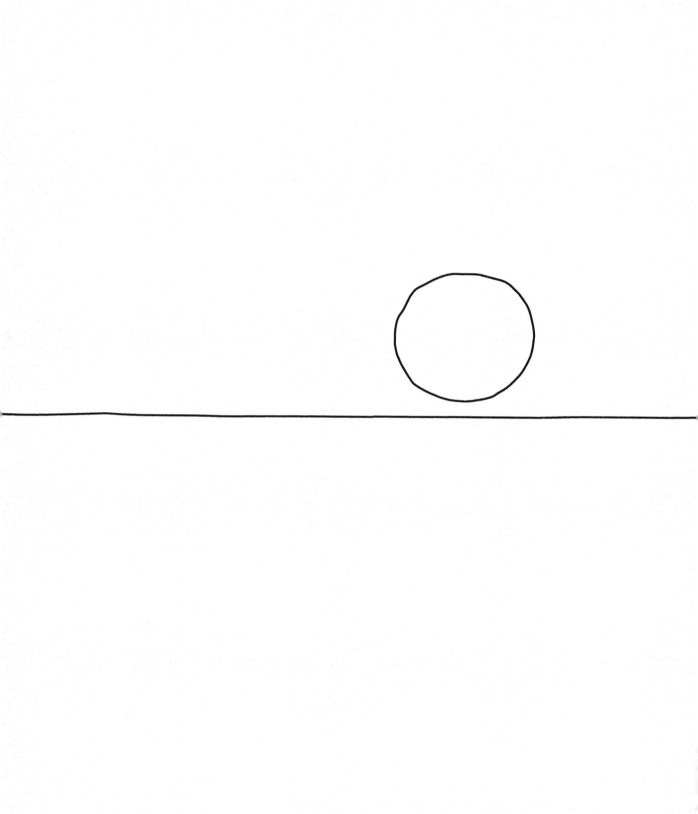

Then,
the
little
triangle
thought,
"I can't do that, but if I don't buy anything else
for a while, I can save enough money to buy the
beautiful circle."

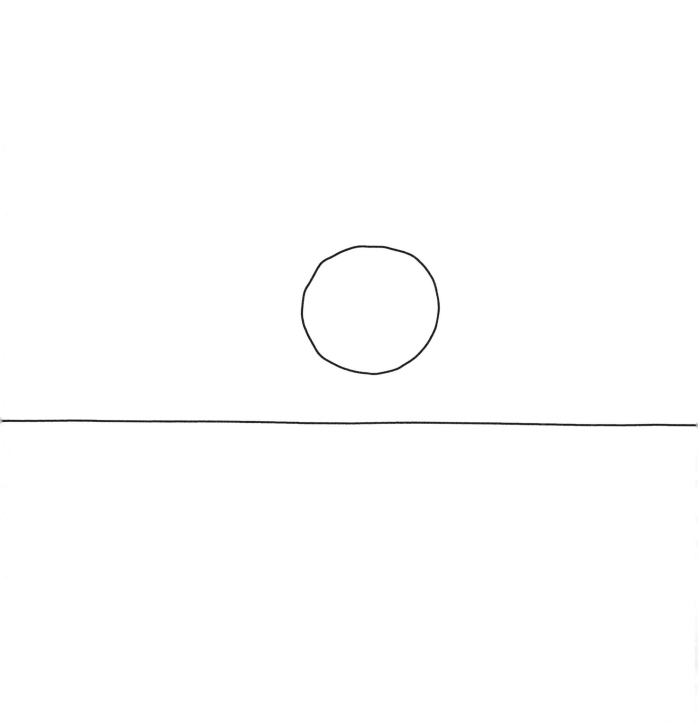

The
little
old
triangle
stopped
buying
things.

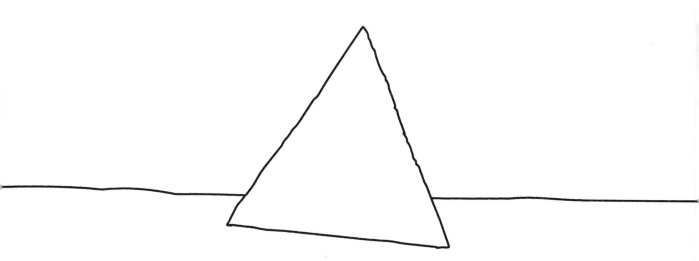

And
he
was
sad.

Every
day
he
had
to
remind
himself
that
soon
he
could
buy
the
beautiful
circle.

"When I was young, I thought it was easy for old triangles to not buy things; but it is never easy,"
the
little
old
triangle
thought.
"I wish I had saved my money when I was young. Then, instead of buying the things I could afford each Saturday, I could have had my beautiful circle for many years."

Finally,
the
little
old
triangle
saved
enough
money
to
buy
the
beautiful
circle.

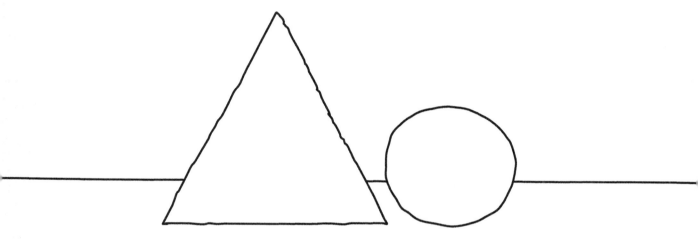

And
the
little
old
triangle
was
happy.

The
beautiful
circle
was
truly
wonderful.

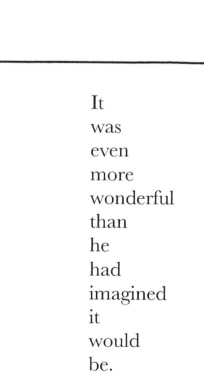

It
was
even
more
wonderful
than
he
had
imagined
it
would
be.

Two
days
later,
the
little
old
triangle
died.

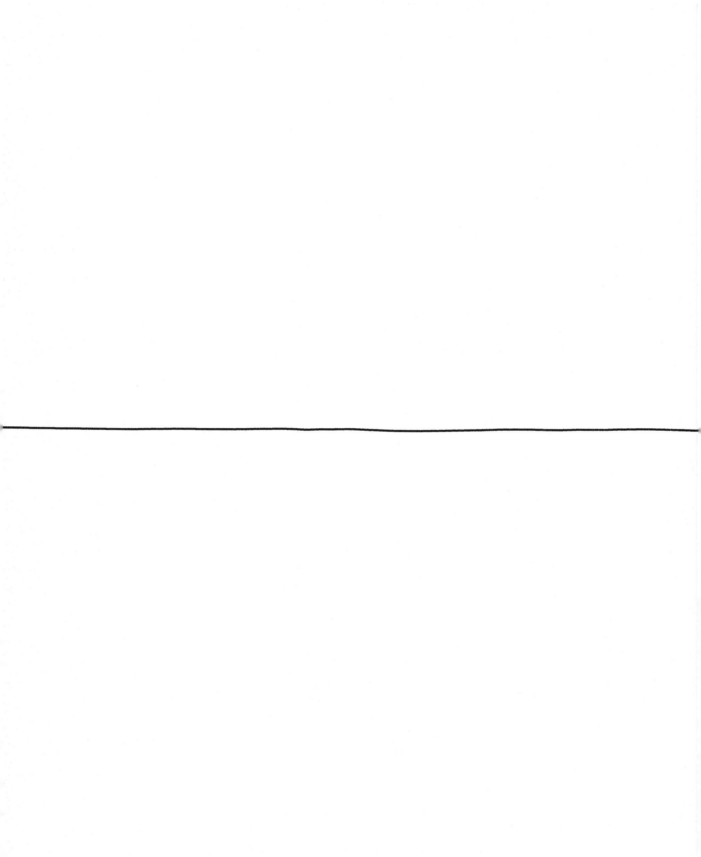

The
beautiful
circle
was
given
to
another
triangle.

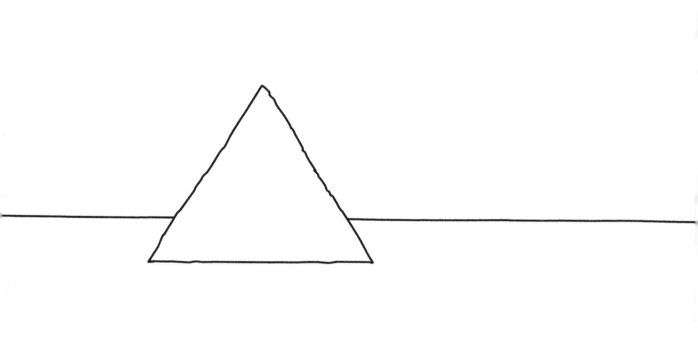

"What's this?"
the
triangle
laughed.
"Why would I want a circle?"

The
triangle
threw
the
beautiful
circle
away.

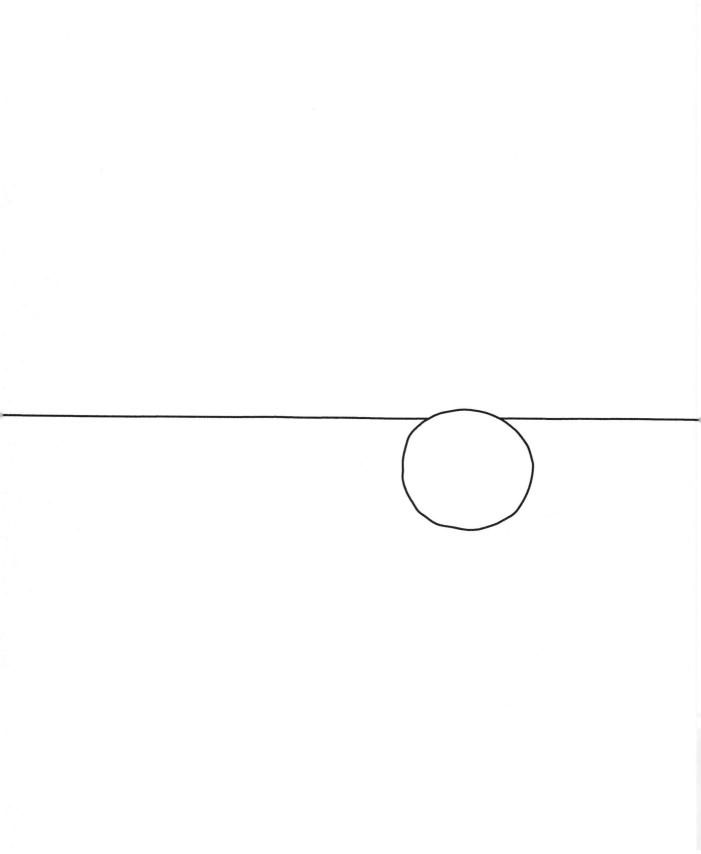

Another
little
triangle
saw
the
beautiful
circle
and
picked
it
up.

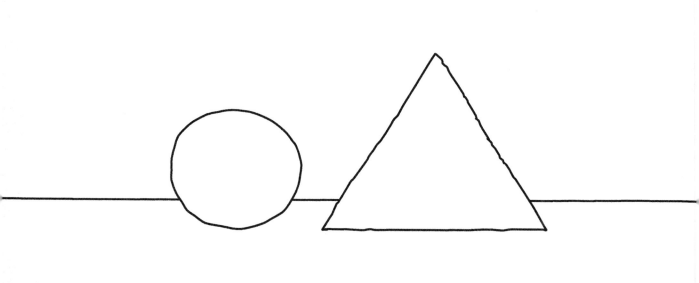

"Oh,"
the
little
triangle
said.
"What a wonderful circle. I am the
luckiest little triangle in the whole
world."

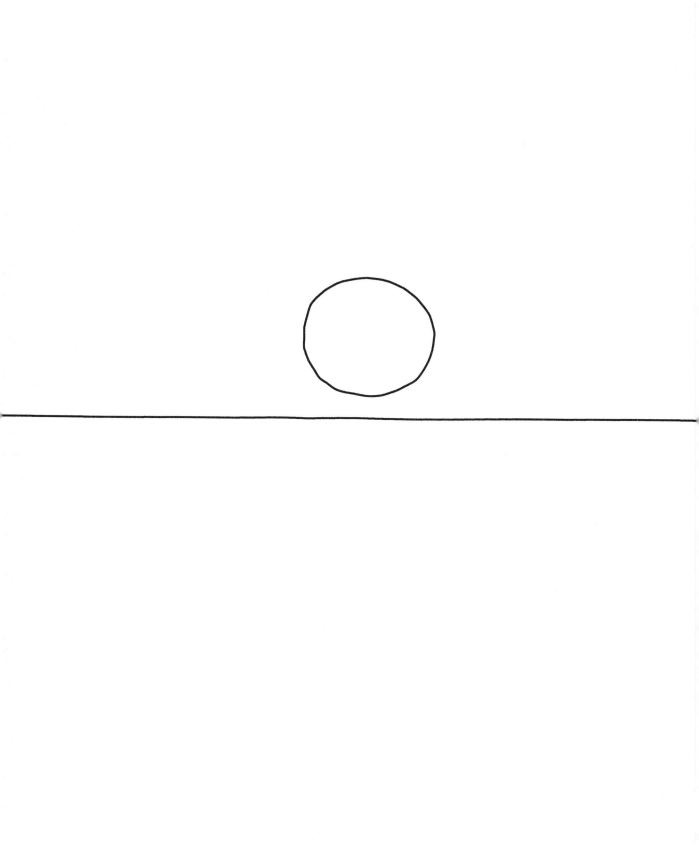

The
little
triangle
brought
the
beautiful
circle
home.

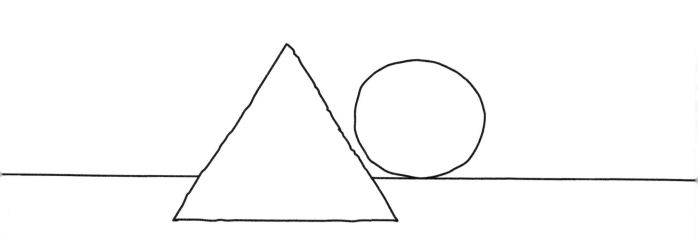

And
the
beautiful
circle
made
that
little
triangle
happy
for
many,
many
years.

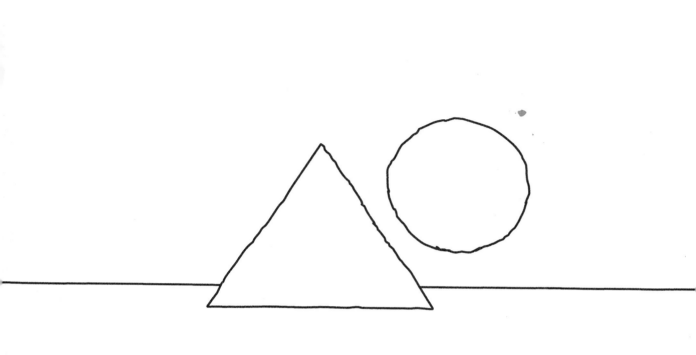

CPSIA information can be obtained at www.ICGtesting.com
Printed in the USA
BVOW08s2041051214

378169BV00004B/29/P

9 780972 361927